Ladybird Readers

MOOMIN

The Song of the Sea

Series Editor: Sorrel Pitts
Text adapted by Mary Taylor

LADYBIRD BOOKS

UK | USA | Canada | Ireland | Australia
India | New Zealand | South Africa

Ladybird Books is part of the Penguin Random House group of companies
whose addresses can be found at global.penguinrandomhouse.com.
www.penguin.co.uk   www.puffin.co.uk   www.ladybird.co.uk

Penguin
Random House
UK

Adapted from the story 'Moomin and the Ocean's Song' first published by Puffin Books, 2016.
This version published by Ladybird Books Ltd, 2019
001

Characters and artwork are the original creation of Tove Jansson

Printed in China

A CIP catalogue record for this book is available from the British Library

ISBN: 978–0–241–36530–4

All correspondence to:
Ladybird Books
Penguin Random House Children's
80 Strand, London WC2R 0RL

MIX
Paper from
responsible sources
FSC® C018179
FSC
www.fsc.org

Ladybird Readers

MOOMIN

The Song
of the Sea

Based on the original stories
by Tove Jansson

Picture words

Moomin

Moominmamma

Moominpappa

Snufkin

Snorkmaiden

Little My

Sniff

the Hattifatteners

shell

storm

lightning

seahorse

recharge

seahorse shoe

Lonely Island

One morning, Moomin worked on his toy boat, and Little My helped him.

Then, they heard a loud noise from upstairs.

"What was that?" asked Moomin.

Moomin and Little My ran
to the top of the house.
Moominpappa was there.

"I came to get something, and these boxes fell on the floor," said Moominpappa.

There were lots of things on the floor.

Moominpappa took a shell from
the floor, and put it next to his ear.

"What beautiful music!" he said.
"It's the song of the sea!"

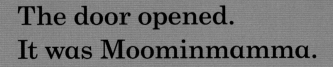

The door opened.
It was Moominmamma.

"What are you all doing?" she asked.

13

"I'm listening to the song of the sea," said Moominpappa.

"I can't hear music!" Little My said, angrily.

"Only the person who found the shell can hear the song," said Moominpappa. "You can't hear it because you didn't find the shell, Little My."

Moomin went for a walk with
Snorkmaiden, and he told her
about the shell.

Snorkmaiden was very excited. "I would like to hear the song of the sea!" she said.

Then, Moomin had an idea.
"Would you like to find a shell with me?" he asked. "A shell for us?"

"Oh! What a nice idea!"
Snorkmaiden said.

"Let's find Snufkin,"
said Moomin.
"He can help us."

"We want a shell that has the song of the sea inside it!" Moomin told Snufkin. "Where can we find one?"

"On Lonely Island!" said Snufkin.

"Do we have to go by boat?" Sniff asked. He was afraid of the water.

"Of course!" said Snufkin.

The weather was sunny and
windy, which was good for
a boat trip.

They were all happy and excited.

"Is that an island?" asked Sniff.

"Yes, it's Lonely Island!"
said Snufkin.

Moomin and Snorkmaiden
saw something in the sea.

"Look!" said Snorkmaiden.

There were two beautiful
animals in the water.

"Seahorses!" said Moomin.
"What pretty colors!"

When the seahorses saw the boat,
they quickly swam under the water.

There were lots of shells on the beach.

"Some of these are prettier than Moominpappa's shell!" Moomin thought.

"I want to find you a shell with the song of the sea inside it!" Moomin said to Snorkmaiden.

Moomin and Snufkin put lots of shells next to their ears, but they couldn't hear the song of the sea.

Moomin found one shell that made
a little noise, but it wasn't music.

"Come here!" Sniff said, quietly.

"Wow! What are they?" asked Snorkmaiden.

"They are the Hattifatteners," said Snufkin.

"What are they doing here?" asked Moomin.

"They come here to recharge,"
Snufkin said. "They take their
light from the lightning."

33

"How do they recharge?"
Moomin asked.

"When there's a storm, they use the lightning to recharge," said Snufkin.

Moomin looked up. It was dark now, and there were lots of clouds in the sky.

Moomin wanted to find a shell
with the song of the sea inside it,
but Snorkmaiden and Sniff
were afraid.

"Let's go back to the boat,"
said Moomin.

They got in their boat,
and left the island.

The lightning, wind, and rain
were terrible! They were all
very frightened.

After many hours, they were
wet, cold, and tired . . .

. . . but they were home, they
were safe, and they were happy!

Moominmamma made some nice, hot tea. "What pretty shells!" she said.

"But my shell doesn't have the song of the sea inside it," Moomin thought, sadly.

When Moomin took his shell from
the table, something small and
beautiful fell out.

"It's a shoe from a seahorse!"
said Moominpappa.

Moominmamma gave
Moomin a box.

"Put the seahorse shoe in here," she said. "Now, you can have a box of nice things, like Moominpappa."

Moomin was very happy!

Activities

The key below describes the skills practiced in each activity.

 Spelling and writing

 Reading

 Speaking

 Critical thinking

 Preparation for the Cambridge Young Learners exams

1 **Look and read. Put a ✓ or a ✗ in the boxes.** 📖 🌼

1  This is Moomin. ✓

2  This is Moominmamma. ✗

3  This is Little My. ✓

4  This is Sniff. ✓

5  These are the Hattifatteners. ✓

6  This is Snorkmaiden. ✓

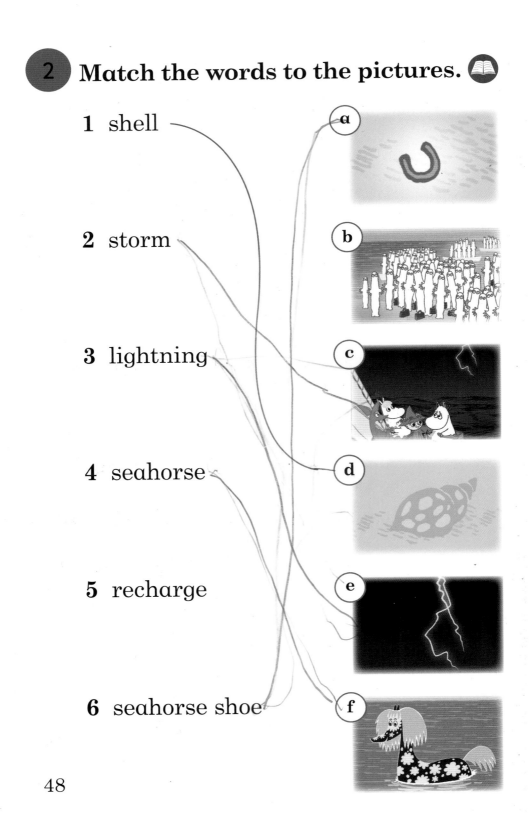

2 Match the words to the pictures.

1 shell

2 storm

3 lightning

4 seahorse

5 recharge

6 seahorse shoe

a

b

c

d

e

f

3 **Read the text. Choose the correct words and write them next to 1—6.**

| fell | top | with | ran | floor | loud |

One morning, Moomin was

1 ___with___ Little My.

They heard a 2 _____ noise

from upstairs, so they 3 _____

to the 4 _____ of the house.

Moominpappa was there. "These boxes

5 _____ on the floor," he said.

There were lots of things

on the 6 _____ .

Circle the correct words.

1 Moominmamma said,
"What are you all **watching?"** /
doing?"

2 "I'm **listening** / **listen** to the song
of the sea," said Moominpappa.

3 Little My was angry because she
couldn't **hear** / **heard** the music.

4 Only the person who **find** / **found**
the shell can hear the song.

5 "You didn't **find** / **found** the shell,
Little My," said Moominpappa.

5 Talk to a friend about the shell.

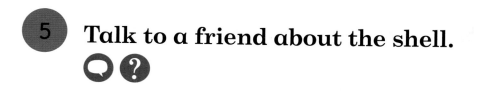

1 Who found the shell?

Moominpappa found the shell.

2 How did he find the shell?

3 What could Moominpappa hear in the shell?

4 Why couldn't Little My hear this?

6 Read and write the correct form of the verbs.

Then, Moomin had an idea. "Would you like to find a shell with me?" he asked. "A shell for us?"

"Oh! What a nice idea!" Snorkmaiden said.

"Let's find Snufkin," said Moomin. "He can help us."

Snorkmaiden ____was____ (be) excited about the shell.

She _____ (want) to hear the song of the sea.

Then, Moomin _____ (have) an idea. "Would you like to find a shell with me?" he _____ (ask).

Snufkin could help them, so they _____ (go) to find him.

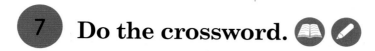
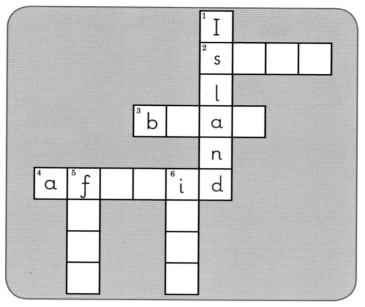

Across

2 Snorkmaiden wanted to hear the . . . of the sea.

3 They had to go to the island by . . .

4 Sniff was . . . of the water.

Down

1 They could find a shell on Lonely . . .

5 Moomin and Snorkmaiden wanted to . . . a shell.

6 Moomin's . . . was to find a shell for Snorkmaiden.

8 **Choose the correct answers.**

The weather was sunny and windy, which was good for a boat trip.

They were all happy and excited.

1 They had to go to Lonely Island . . .

   a on foot.

   b by boat.

2 The weather was . . .

   a windy and rainy.

   b sunny and windy.

3 The weather was . . . for a boat trip.

   a good

   b bad

4 They were all happy and . . .

   a hungry.

   b excited.

9 **Match the two parts of the sentences. Then, write them on the lines.**

1 Sniff saw an island. It

2 Moomin and Snorkmaiden

3 They were in a boat and

a saw something in the sea.

b the sea was pink.

c was Lonely Island.

1 Sniff saw an island. It was Lonely Island.

2

3

10 **Ask and answer the questions with a friend.**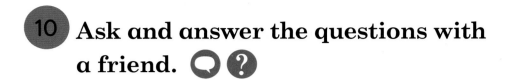

1
> *What were the animals?*

> *They were seahorses.*

2 How many seahorses did they see?

3 What colors were the seahorses?

4 What did the seahorses do when they saw the boat?

5 Do seahorses live in the sea?

11 **Find the words.**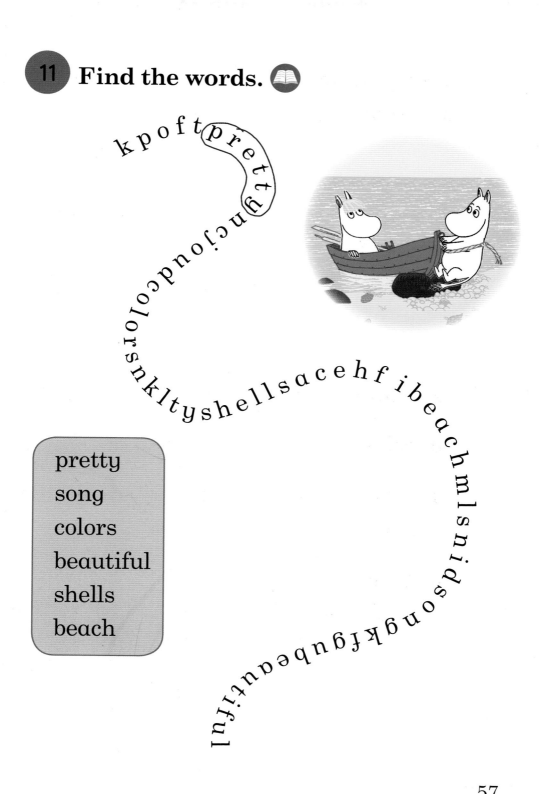

kpoftpretty...gncjoudcolorsnkltyshellsacehfibeachmlsnidsongktgubeautiful

pretty
song
colors
beautiful
shells
beach

12 **Complete the sentences.**
Write a—d.

1 There were lots of ....b............

2 They put lots of shells ....

3 They couldn't hear ....

4 One shell made a noise, ...

> **a** next to their ears.
>
> **b** shells on the beach.
>
> **c** but it wasn't music.
>
> **d** the song of the sea.

13 **Read the text. Choose the correct words and write them next to 1—4.**

1 seeing	sees	saw
2 recharging	recharge	recharged
3 who	what	when
4 their	there	they're

1 Moomin and his friends .... s a w ....

the Hattifatteners on Lonely Island.

2 The Hattifatteners come to the island

to ....

3 They recharge .... there

is a storm.

4 They take .... light from

the lightning.

14 **Read the answers. Write the questions.**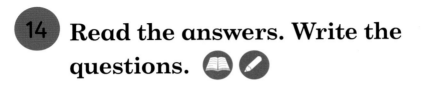

1 How do the Hattifatteners recharge?

They use the light from lightning to recharge.

2 _____

_____

He saw lots of clouds in the sky.

3 _____

_____

Snorkmaiden and Sniff were afraid.

4 _____

_____

Because of the lightning, wind and rain.

15 **Write the questions.**

1 is Where Moomin ?

   Where is Moomin?

2 leave the Did island they ?

   ....

3 the Was terrible weather ?

   ....

4 very they Were frightened ?

   ....

5 get home they Did ?

   ....

16 **Look, match, and write the words.**

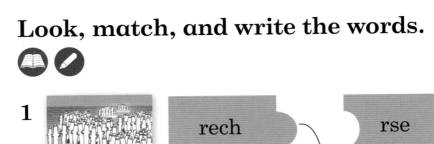

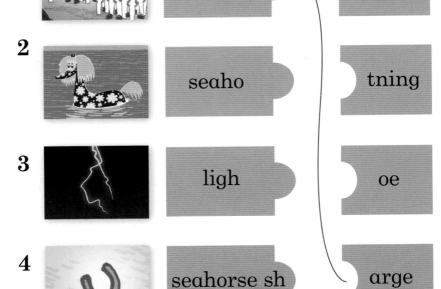

1		rech	rse
2		seaho	tning
3		ligh	oe
4		seahorse sh	arge

1   recharge

2

3

4

17 Write about your favorite part of the story. Why is it your favorite? ✏️ ❓

My favorite part of the story is . . .

Level 3

The Jungle Book

978–0–241–25383–0 ☐

The Red Knight

978–0–241–25384–7 ☐

The Elves and the Shoemaker

978–0–241–25385–4 ☐

Rapunzel

978–0–241–28394–3 ☐

Puss in Boots

978–0–241–28407–0 ☐

Jack and the Beanstalk

978–0–241–28397–4 ☐

Hansel and Gretel

978–0–241–29861–9 ☐

Snow White and the Seven Dwarfs

978–0–241–31955–0 ☐

The Talent Show

978–0–241–29859–6 ☐

Minibeasts

978–0–241–28404–9 ☐

Sharks

978–0–241–25382–3 ☐

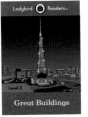

Great Buildings

978–0–241–28400–1 ☐

A Great Night!

978–0–241–29863–3 ☐

The Pony School News

978–0–241–31611–5 ☐

The Song of the Sea

978–0–241–36530–4 ☐

Bumblebee and the Rock Concert

978–0–241–29867–1 ☐

A History of Ferrari

978–0–241–36509–0 ☐

Ice Worlds

978–0–241–31957–4 ☐

Where Animals Live

978–0–241–29868–8 ☐

Now you're ready for Level 4!